GUITAR
TUNES
FOR CHILDREN
Anthony Marks

Designed by Doriana Berkovic
Edited by Jenny Tyler

Illustrated by Simone Abel
and Kim Blundell

Music selected, arranged and edited by Anthony Marks
New compositions by Anthony Marks
Guitar advisor: Mark Marrington
Music setting: Andrew Jones

About this book

You will already know some of these tunes, though others might be less familiar. Some of them were written specially for this book. If you have a computer, you can listen to all the tunes on the Usborne Quicklinks Website to hear how they go. Just go to **www.usborne-quicklinks.com** and enter the keywords "guitar tunes for children", then follow the simple instructions.

At the start of every piece there is a picture in a circle. Each picture has a sticker to match it in the middle of the book. Use the stickers to show when you have learned a piece.

Contents

Guitar reminders

Here are some hints to help you enjoy guitar playing more. You can read these first, or go straight to the music on page 4 and come back here if you want some reminders.

If you need to know the fingering for a particular note, there is a chart on page 32 showing how to play all the notes in this book.

Getting comfortable

When you play the guitar, it is important to feel relaxed so that your fingers can move easily. The best way to do this is to rest the guitar on your left leg, raised up a little. (You can use a special support so that your leg is in the right position for this.) With the guitar in this position, it is easier to see the fingerboard and your left hand will be relaxed all the way up the neck.

Keep your back straight but not stiff.

The guitar neck should point upwards slightly.

Rest your right arm on top of the guitar.

Make sure the guitar is upright (not sloping forwards or backwards).

Sit on the front part of the chair.

You could use a support for your left foot.

Left hand and fingers

Hold your left thumb straight out. Place it on the back of the guitar neck, about in line with the second fret.
 Curve your fingers over the strings so that when you press them down your fingertips are at right angles to the strings.

Press the strings firmly just to the left of the fretwire.

Your fingernails need to be fairly short.

Keep your hand and wrist relaxed.

Don't press too hard.

Plucking the strings

To play the tunes in this book, you need to pluck the strings in different ways. For most of the pieces, pluck with your index and middle fingers. Keep each finger straight. Pull upwards on the string, plucking towards your face, and let your finger rest on the next string. This is called rest stroke. In other pieces you will need a style of playing called free stroke. Keep your fingers curved and pluck outwards, away from the guitar.
 For some of the pieces you need to use your thumb. Keep it straight, and pluck the string by pushing downwards, away from your face. Make sure only your thumb moves, not your whole hand.

Turn the glasses over

This is a sailor's song called a sea shanty. "Shanty" comes from the French word "chanter", which means "to sing".

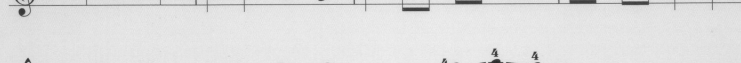

Solveig's song

This tune is based on a Norwegian folk song. In 1875 the Norwegian composer Grieg used it in his music for "Peer Gynt", a play by Henrik Ibsen. Watch out for the accidentals.

The jolly farmer

The German composer Schumann wrote this in 1848. It is one of a group of pieces for young people called "Album for the Young".

Basse danse

The "basse danse" is a graceful, gliding dance that was popular in France in the 16th century. This tune was first published in 1558.

Will the circle be unbroken

This religious tune was probably first sung by slaves or poor farmers in the 19th century in America. You can play this in second position throughout, or move between first and second.

Early one morning

"Early one morning" is an old English folk song. Try playing different sections loud and soft. Can you make an echo effect with the two phrases that start on B?

You have to play a fingered note in the lower part - find out more opposite.

Home on the range

Brewster Higley and Daniel Kelley wrote this in America in the 1870s. You have to play some fingered notes in the lower part - find out more below.

Fingered notes in the lower part

For some of the tunes in this book, you have to use your left-hand fingers for notes in both the upper and lower parts. To do this, sometimes your fingers have to make unusual shapes on the fingerboard. Follow the fingerings carefully it will make the pieces easier to play. Here are some hints to help you.

Learn the top part first. Make sure you follow the fingering carefully. Play the top part with your right-hand fingers.

Next, learn the lower part. Again, follow the left-hand fingering very carefully. Play the lower part with your right-hand thumb.

When you feel confident with both parts, try playing them together. It may help to go slowly at first, then speed up.

Simple gifts

Joseph Brackett, a member of an American religious group known as the Shakers, wrote this in 1848. Follow the fingering carefully.

Barcarolle

This was written by the French composer Jacques Offenbach in the 19th century. A barcarolle is a boating song - play it softly and gently.

D. C. al Fine

8

Rigadoon

This tune was written in the 17th century by Purcell, an English composer. You can play it as a duet (a tune for two players).

Playing duets

Play your own line until you know it well. It can help to learn both parts, so you know what the other person's music will sound like. Then, when you play with someone else, count a few bars together before you start so that you begin at the same time. When you both know the music, try exchanging parts.

You could record one part and play the other over the top

You can download duet parts from the Internet (see page 2).

The sailor woman

Nobody knows who wrote this tune. It was first published in the 17th century in France, but is probably much older than that.

Russian folk tune

Look out for top B flat (string 1, fret 6, finger 4).

This tune is in third position. Move your left hand up the neck to play the first note: string 2, fret 3, finger 1. Your hand stays in this position for the whole piece.

When you know this well, try starting it on E (string 4, fret 2, finger 2).

Two by two

This tune is also known as "When Johnny comes marching home". Patrick Gilmore, an American bandmaster, wrote it in the 1860s.

Galumphing!

Trumpet tune

The English composer Purcell wrote this in the 17th century. You have to move between third and first position. Follow the fingering carefully.

Joyfully

As you move between positions, keep your left elbow relaxed. Make sure your thumb moves up the guitar neck with the rest of your hand.

11

Nkosi sikelel iAfrika

The English title of this tune is "Lord bless Africa". It was written in 1897 by Enoch Sontonga, and is now the national anthem of South Africa. See opposite for more about *p*, *i*, *m* and *a*.

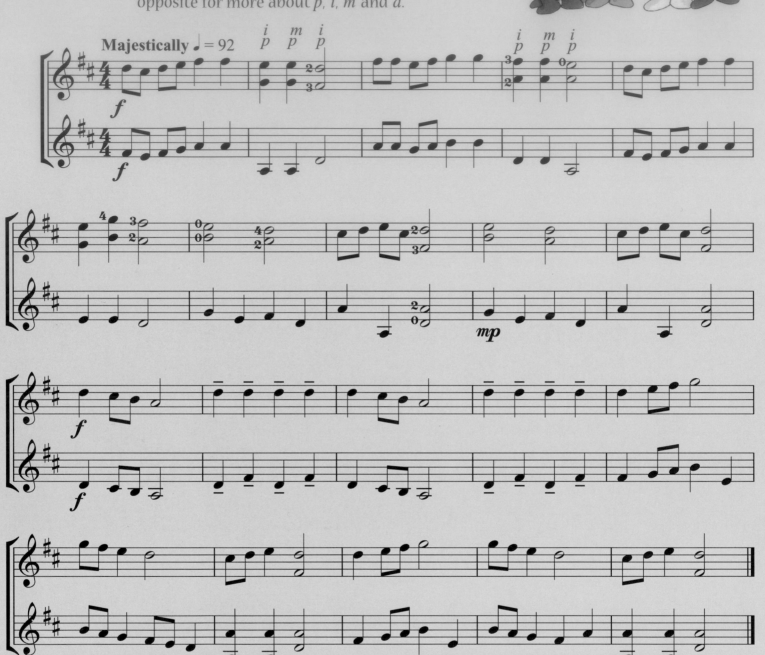

Playing two notes at once

The top part in this piece contains some two-note chords on the higher strings. Play the lower note of each chord with your right thumb. For the top note of each chord, alternate between your index (first) and middle (second) fingers, using free stroke.

Allegro

This piece was written by Mauro Giuliani, an Italian guitarist and composer who lived in the 19th century. It needs special right-hand fingering - see below.

Right-hand fingers

In this piece, the upper line is an accompaniment and the tune is in the lower line. To make the lower notes stand out, pluck them quite firmly with your thumb.

In some guitar music you will see letters by the notes which suggest which right-hand fingers to use. The diagram on the right tells you more. If you use the fingers of your right hand as shown in the music, this will help to make the upper notes smooth and even.

m = middle (second) finger

i = index (first) finger

a = ring (third) finger

p = thumb

Gathering peascods

This old English tune was first published in a book called "The Dancing Master" (find out more on pages 18 and 19).

Air (from the "Water Music")

The Water Music was written in 1717 by the composer Handel, for a procession on the River Thames by King George I of England.

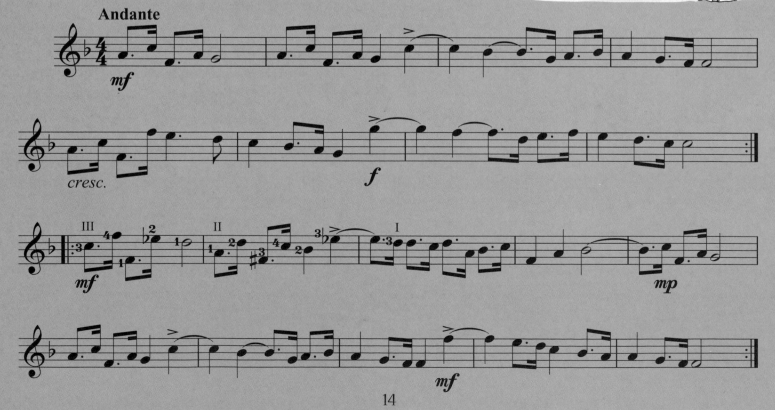

Greensleeves

"Greensleeves" was first printed in the 16th century. Some people say that King Henry VIII of England wrote it, but this may be just a legend.

Not too quickly

Tuning

Before you play, tune your guitar so that the strings play the right notes. This is especially important when you play duets so that both guitars are in tune with each other. You can tune up using pitch-pipes, a tuning fork, an electronic tuner or a keyboard.

Once string 6 is in tune, you can tune all the other notes from it. This is called relative tuning.

Play string 6, fret 5 and tune string 5 to match it. Then play string 5, fret 5 and tune string 4 to match it. Then play string 4, fret 5 and tune string 3 to match. To hear the note to tune your second string to, play string 3 fret 4 (not fret 5). Finish by tuning string 1 to string 2, fret 5.

Simon's tune

This tune was written by Jacob van Eyck, a Dutch composer who lived from 1590 to 1657. You have to play many of the lower notes in third position.

Not too quickly

Drink to me only

This old English song was written in the 17th century. Ask another guitarist to play the chords (find out more below).

Andante

Chords

To accompany tunes, you can use chords (groups of notes played at the same time). Chords are shown by letters above the music. Ask someone else to play the chords while you play the tune, then change over. (If there is just you, the tunes still work without the chords.)

For each chord, you need to learn where to put your left-hand fingers, and which strings to play. There are special diagrams to help you. On page 32 you can find all the chord diagrams you need for this book.

16

La follia

This very old Portuguese tune became popular all over Europe in the 16th century. "La follia" is Italian for "foolishness".

Adagio ♩ = 66

Ma Normandie

A French composer, Frédéric Bérat, wrote this in 1836. Bérat was born in Rouen, a city in Normandy.

A bit sadly

CII (throughout)

In this piece, CII tells you to hold a barre across strings 1-4 at the second fret all the way through. (Don't press too hard or your hand will get tired.)

You can play this tune at any fret by moving your left hand up or down the neck.

Jenny pluck pears

This tune is from "The Dancing Master", a book that was first published in London in 1651 by a musician and bookseller named Thomas Playford. Look out for bottom B flat in the lower part.

Watch each other carefully when you slow down in the last line, so that you reach the end together.

18

The trout

Franz Schubert, an Austrian composer, wrote this tune around 1817. Don't let go of the long notes in the top part while playing the shorter notes below them.

Easter Tuesday

This tune is also from "The Dancing Master". Playford listed steps for each tune so that people could learn the dances.

The fairy queen

This tune is by the English composer Henry Purcell. "The fairy queen" is a play with music. It was first performed in 1692. You have to move between first and third positions in this piece.

When you get to the end, play the first section again.

Not too slowly

D. C. al fine

Dream of you

This tune was written specially for this book. Try to emphasize the notes in the lower part, but play the upper notes smoothly and evenly.

Take your time!

The ash grove

"The ash grove" is an old Welsh song. You play the second part in fifth position. Move your hand up the neck until your first finger is on the fifth fret. Then move back down into first position to play the repeat.

Les trois rois

This is an old Christmas carol from Provence in southern France. The title means "The three kings". Play it all in fifth position. You don't need to move your hand on the neck.

We three kings

This tune was written in the 19th century by an American composer, J. H. Hopkins.

Deck the halls

"Deck the halls" is an old Christmas tune that was first sung in Wales. Play it brightly and cheerfully. Follow the fingering carefully when you move to second position.

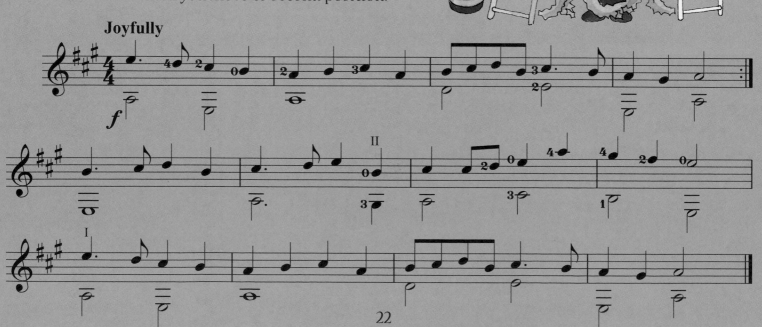

Go, tell it on the mountain

This Christmas tune was sung by slaves in the southern USA. It was published in 1907 by an African-American composer, Henry Clay Work. For the top line of this piece, you have to change between second and fifth position. Follow the fingering carefully.

Touchy-feely

This duet was written specially for this book. When you reach the end of the music, don't forget to go back and play the first part again.

Different ways of playing duets

When you play duets, it is fun to experiment with tempo (how fast and slow to play) and dynamics (how loud and quiet). However it helps if both players make these changes together.

For instance, if you both get louder or quieter at the same time it is more effective than if one player changes dynamic without the other. Plan the changes you want to make and mark the music to remind you of them.

The Arethusa

The Arethusa was an English battleship in the 18th century. This song was written in the 1790s by William Shield and Prince Hoare.

Allegro molto

Shenandoah

Shenandoah was a Native American chief who lived by the Missouri River. The tune became popular in the 1820s, but it may be older.

Slowly and sadly   CIII (throughout)

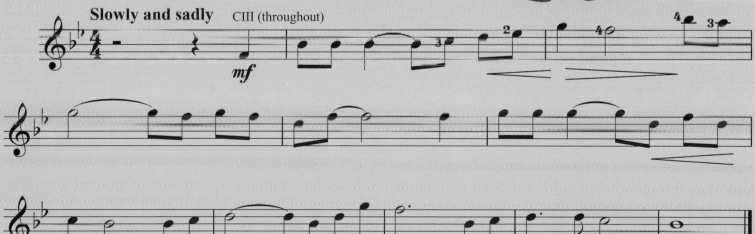

Hold down a four-string barre at the third fret throughout this piece.

By moving your left hand up and down the neck, you can play this tune at any fret.

Try starting on G (string 4, fret 5, finger 1). How many different starting notes can you find? Moving a tune around like this is called transposing.

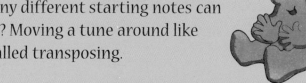

25

Prelude

This piece was written by Dionisio Aguado, a Spanish guitarist and composer who lived from 1789 to 1849.

Full moon tune

This tune was written specially for this book. Play quietly and make the music sound mysterious. "1/2CV" tells you to barre strings 1, 2 and 3 at fret 5.

Liliburlero

This old Irish tune was first published in "The Dancing Master" (see page 18). This version is for up to four players - find out more below.

Ways to play "Liliburlero"

The middle line of music is the tune, so learn this first. Then ask someone to accompany you, using either the chord symbols or the lowest line of music. Then get someone else to add the top line, which is an extra part to decorate the tune.

If there are four of you, use all three lines of music and the chords. Play the tune several times. To vary it each time, exchange parts or leave different lines out. Experiment with tempo and dynamics too (see page 24).

Humming song

This piece by Schumann is from "Album for the Young" (see page 5). Try to play it evenly and smoothly.

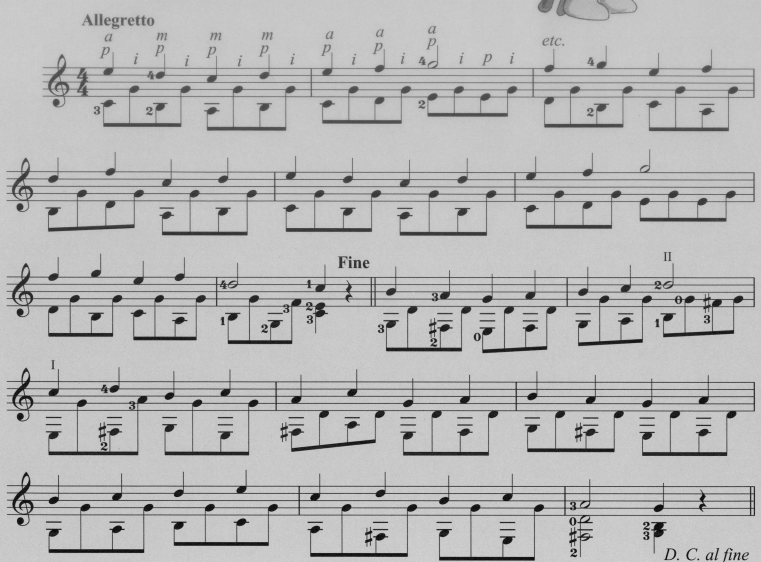

Arrangements

Schumann wrote "Humming song" for piano, but it works well for guitar too. A new version of a piece for a different instrument (or group of instruments) is called an arrangement.

Here are some ideas to help you make new arrangements of tunes in this book. Ask other people to play with you, or use the Internet files (see page 2). You will need to experiment until you find versions that you like. Can you write your ideas down so that you remember them next time you play?

• Add chords to pieces like "Greensleeves" (page 15) or "Full moon tune" (page 26).

• Invent new parts like the top line of "Liliburlero" (page 27). Experiment to find notes that fit (long notes work best at first).

• Someone could play the tunes with you on another instrument, such as a recorder or violin. For tunes with more than one line (like "Humming song"), the other instrument should play the slower notes.

Three into two

This duet was written specially for this book. To think in 5/4 for this tune, count a group of three then a group of two in each bar. (Don't rush the group of two.)

Watch out for top B flat (string 1, fret 6).

The lower part in this piece contains unusual chord shapes. Follow the fingerings carefully. They may feel tricky at first but will get easier with practice.
   Try playing "Three into two" at different speeds. Which sounds best? Is it better loud or quiet? When you have decided, you could write tempo and dynamic directions on the music.

Andante in A minor

This tune is by Ferdinando Carulli, an Italian guitarist and composer who lived from 1770 to 1841.

Packington's pound

This old English tune was written for the lute (a stringed instrument that was popular before the guitar was invented).

Minuet in G

This piece was written by the German composer J. S. Bach (1685-1750). You could try learning the two lines separately then put them together.

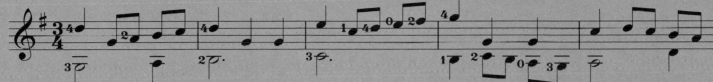

Waltz

This tune was written by Jose Ferrer, a Spanish composer who lived from 1835 to 1916. The numbers in circles remind you which strings to play when you are in higher positions.

Notes in this book

The notes used in this book are shown on the chart below. Many notes on the guitar can be played on different strings at different frets, so you need to look at the music for hints about where to play each note and which fingers to use.

Some notes have two names - a sharp name and a flat name. The name you use depends on the key of the piece you are playing. In some places, the chart shows both names. This is because both versions of the note are used in the book.

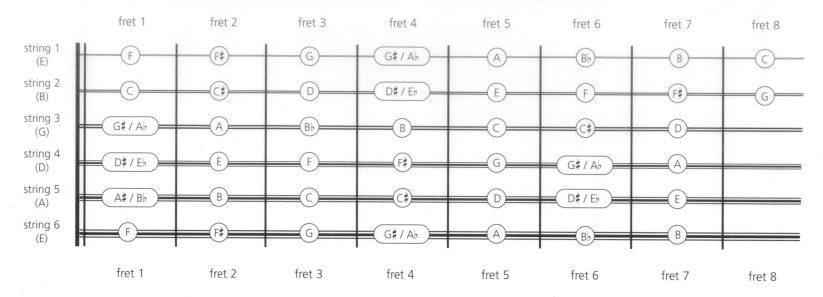

Chords

This chart shows you how to play the chords in this book. The vertical lines are the strings (the sixth string is furthest to the left). The horizontal lines are the frets. The circles show you where to put your fingers. The numbers in the circles show you which finger to use. An 0 above a string tells you to play an open string. A cross tells you not to play that string at all. Where you see the word "barre", hold your first finger flat across the strings shown.

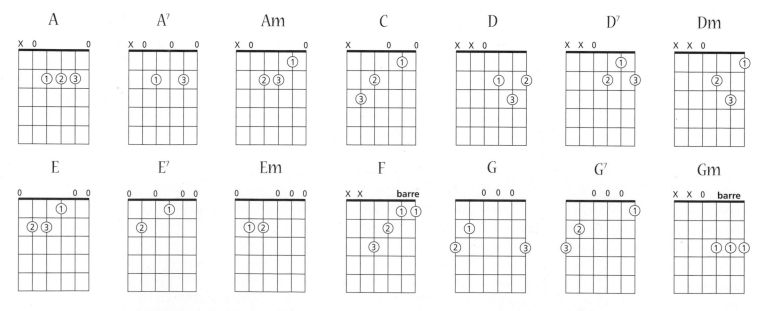

First published in 2004 by Usborne Publishing Ltd, Usborne House, 83-85 Saffron Hill, London EC1N 8RT, England.
www.usborne.com